CANAL PIONEERS

From Brindley to Telford and Beyond

CHRIS MORRIS

TANNER'S YARD PRESS

First published 2012 by Tanners Yard Press

Tanners Yard Press Church Road Longhope GL17 0LA
www.tannersyardpress.co.uk

Designed by Paul Manning

Printed and bound by Ozgraf, Poland

British Library Cataloguing in Publication Data
A catalogue record for this book is available from the British Library

ISBN 978 09564358 3 5

Contents

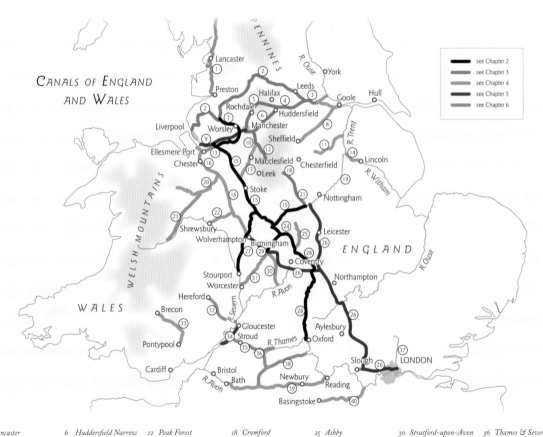

CANALS OF ENGLAND AND WALES

1 Lancaster	*6* Huddersfield Narrow	*12* Peak Forest	*18* Cromford	*25* Ashby	*30* Stratford-upon-Avon	*36* Thames & Severn
2 Leeds & Liverpool	*7* Bridgewater	*13* Weaver Navigation	*19* Trent Navigation	*26* Grand Union	*31* Worcester &	*37* Lea Navigation
3 Aire & Calder	*8* Sheffield & South	*14* Fossdyke	*20* Llangollen	*27* Staffordshire &	Birmingham	*38* Berkshire & Wiltshire
Navigation	Yorkshire	*15* Trent & Mersey	*21* Erewash	Worcestershire	*32* Hereford & Gloucester	*39* Kennet & Avon
4 Calder & Hebble	*9* Manchester Ship	*16* Shrophire Union	*22* Shrewsbury	*28* Oxford	*33* Brecon & Monmouth	*40* Basingstoke
Navigation	*10* Ashton	(Main Line)	*23* Montgomeryshire	*29* Birmingham and	*34* Sharpness	
5 Rochdale	*11* Chesterfield	*17* Macclesfield	*24* Coventry	Fazely Canals	*35* Stroudwater	

FOREWORD

The aim of this portfolio of modern photographs is to celebrate the legacy of the canal pioneers. It is preceded by a set of illustrated biographical notes of some of the prominent early engineers. While not being a comprehensive guide, *Canal Pioneers* offers a wide-ranging set of views of many of Britain's canals, combining historic engineering with modern usage.

Despite a century of neglect, the spirit of enterprise is alive and well on Britain's canals again. Today's pioneers are not only the restoration societies and volunteers, but also the thousands of enthusiastic but sometimes inexperienced holidaymakers who become bargees for a week or two.

Fossdyke, connecting Lincoln to the River Trent, built by the Romans in AD 120

1
THE CANAL PIONEERS

It is widely accepted that James Brindley built the first canal in Britain for the Duke of Bridgewater, to get his coal to market more efficiently. This claim is only true if the many improved river navigations are ignored, and the Romans' Fossdyke, connecting Lincoln to the River Trent, discounted. Viewing wider horizons, canals had been in existence in China since at least the second century, mainly as extensions of navigable rivers It was not until the tenth century that the concept of a pound lock with mitred gates up and downstream hugely increased the potential usefulness of a canal, enabling it to cross hills and valleys instead of having to follow the contours of the landscape.

By the middle of the eighteenth century, transport of supplies to, and products from, the factories of Britain's embryonic Industrial Revolution was mainly by packhorse, cart or by river. Few river navigations had pound locks; instead, the weirs had removable sections (flash locks), through which boats travelling upstream had to be hauled against the rush of water. Indeed, efforts to improve river navigation by raising water levels with weirs and pound locks were fiercely opposed by the vested interests of mill owners, fishermen and the teams of men who hauled the boats.

James Brindley 1716–1772
Brindley grew up in rural Cheshire with little formal education; aged seventeen, he was apprenticed to a millwright – today he would be called a mechanical engineer. By the middle of the century he was working on his own account with a growing reputation, and his designs for machinery for draining colliery levels caught the attention of the Duke of Bridgewater, owner of coal mines north of Manchester.

The duke had recently returned from a 'Grand Tour' very impressed with the Canal du Midi, which had been built a century earlier to connect the French Atlantic and Mediterranean coasts. On a much more modest scale, he wondered whether a canal could be cut to help him transport coal from the mines at Worsley to the navigable River Irwell. Could Brindley be the man to help? In the event, Brindley went beyond the duke's concept: rather than taking locks down to the river for trans-shipment, he argued that the canal should stay on its level, crossing the Irwell on an aqueduct and heading straight to a wharf in Manchester.

The Bridgewater Canal opened in 1761 and was the first canal to take a route independent of a river valley. In a world about to be transformed by the Industrial Revolution, it drew attention

Towpath bridge across the Staffordshire & Worcestershire at Haywood where it joins the Trent & Mersey

connected by canal. The biggest element was the Trent & Mersey Canal, running from the navigable Trent in Derbyshire to join the existing Bridgewater at Runcorn. The other canals forming the 'cross' were, from the Severn, the Worcestershire & Staffordshire, and a combination of the Coventry & Oxford heading south to the Thames. The connections of all these canals were to the north of the industrial heartland of Birmingham, which had its own network and connections to the 'cross'.

After the Bridgewater, Brindley's most famous work was a tunnel under Harecastle Hill whose completion held up the opening of the Trent & Mersey until after his death. Brindley's hallmark had been to minimise locks and earthworks by making his canals follow the contours of the land where possible. This meant the routes followed convoluted meanders, which, as the pace of life speeded up towards the end of the eighteenth century, were seen as inefficient. As we shall see, the following generation of engineers would take an increasingly forthright view, straightening Brindley's 'country lane' routes and building new canals as if they were motorways.

for two other reasons: one was the amazing sight of coal barges high in the sky crossing the Irwell on the Barton Aqueduct; the other, the fact that the canal enabled the price of coal in the city to be halved.

The economic and practical benefits were not missed by industrialists, who had hitherto had to transport their raw materials and finished products by cart or pack horse to navigable rivers. Brindley was in much demand, first extending the Bridgewater to Runcorn on the Mersey, then beginning to put into practice his 'Grand Cross' concept, which saw England's four main rivers, the Thames, Severn, Trent and Mersey all

John Smeaton 1724–1792

Smeaton had an unusually academic background. When he left Leeds Grammar School, he worked in his father's law firm but switched to become a mathematical instrument-maker. His election as a fellow of the Royal Society in 1753 can be seen as confirmation of his ability to combine practical and theoretical knowledge.

Bowling, west of Glasgow, where the Forth & Clyde Canal meets the sea

On the practical side, Smeaton was commissioned to build a replacement Eddystone lighthouse, using a lime mortar he invented that set underwater. His main canal achievements were the Calder & Hebble Navigation and the Forth & Clyde Canal, connecting the coasts in central Scotland.

A member of the intellectual 'Lunar Society', Smeaton was highly regarded by his peer group and set up a society for civil engineers (he coined the term to distinguish their work from the military). After his death it was known as 'the Smithsonian' and was a forerunner of the Institution of Civil Engineers. Generous in his handing-on of knowledge, one of his pupils was William Jessop, of whom more later.

Josiah Clowes 1735–1794

Clowes' early involvement with canals was as a partner with Hugh Henshall in a carrying company. When Brindley died in 1772 with the Trent & Mersey still unfinished, Henshall took on the job of engineer. Clowes acted as a contractor on the building of locks, and was probably involved with Harecastle Hill tunnel.

After a spell with the Chester Canal he moved to Gloucestershire to help Thomas Dadford with the Stroudwater, and then Robert Whitworth with the Thames & Severn, where he was engineer for the Sapperton Tunnel.

West portal of the Sapperton Tunnel, on the Thames & Severn Canal

Whitworth moved on and left Clowes to supervise the construction of the Sapperton Tunnel, at the time the longest in the world. The success of this project left him with the reputation as a tunnelling expert and he was in high demand, working for the Worcester & Birmingham, Hereford & Gloucester and Leeds & Liverpool.

Considering his real achievements, it is unfortunate that Clowes' claim to fame rests on none of these, but on the remains of an aqueduct on the Shrewsbury canal. Crossing the River Tern at Longdon, this took the form of a conventionally massive brick arch, suited to take the weight of puddled clay, but Clowes died before it was finished. Thomas Telford took over the work and, with the help of ironmaster William Reynolds, utilised an iron trough standing on braced iron supports to bridge the river. The remains still stand in a quiet pasture, a monument to Telford's genius, though a rather muted comment on that of Clowes.

Llanfoist wharf, on the Brecon Canal

Thomas Dadford 1761–1801

Thomas Dadford came from a family of canal engineers: his father and two brothers were all involved in canal-building, mostly in South Wales. Thomas assisted his father, Thomas senior, on the Glamorganshire and on the Neath canals, then became engineer for the Leominster.

Much of his short life was spent with the Monmouthshire & Brecon Canal; the most significant structures in his legacy are fourteen locks and an aqueduct over the Usk at Brynich.

Benjamin Outram 1764–1805

Outram's first involvement with canal work arose as his father was a promoter of the Cromford Canal; when William Jessop was appointed engineer, Outram junior became his assistant. During the digging of Butterley tunnel, mineral deposits were revealed, and Outram contrived to take a fifty percent stake (with the company secretary) in the land. Thus, his initial involvement with canal engineering was rapidly matched by a big business in iron, lime and collieries.

*Rail and canal warehouse at Whaley Bridge
at the terminus of the Peak Forest Canal*

As well as his canal projects at Derby and Nottingham, Outram was an advocate of tramways (the need for rails providing a market for his ironworks), and was the builder of the famous Pen-y-Darren in South Wales, where Trevithick won his wager on the efficacy of steam locomotion. His biggest appointment was as consulting engineer for the Huddersfield Narrow Canal and its gigantic Standedge Tunnel. He should also be remembered for the Holmes Aqueduct on the Derby Canal, a single span of iron completed just before Telford's at Longdon-upon-Tern.

William Jessop 1745–1814

Jessop's father, Josias, was a shipwright in Devonport naval dockyard; when the Eddystone lighthouse burnt down in 1755, he was given the job of implementing Smeaton's plan for the replacement. When Josias died, Smeaton became guardian to young William and took him on as an assistant. After gaining experience working with Smeaton on the Calder navigations, Jessop went to Ireland to take charge of the difficult Grand Canal.

The Grand Junction Canal near Blisworth

By the last decade of the century, Jessop was a very busy man. Modest by nature, he had no objections to working in tandem with less experienced engineers, which led him into a partnership with Outram in the Butterley Ironworks (see above) and a working relationship with Thomas Telford on the Ellesmere and the Caledonian Canals (see below). Probably he is best remembered for his work on the Grand Junction, cut as a more direct route from Birmingham to London than Brindley's meandering Oxford Canal.

Jessop's expertise was not confined to canals: in 1800 he was responsible for West India Docks beside the Thames in London, and in 1801 was appointed chief engineer to the Surrey Iron Railway, having advised that a canal would demand too much water.

John Rennie 1761–1821

Rennie was born into a farming family in the East Lothian district of Scotland. He worked his way up from the village school to graduate from Edinburgh University in 1783. He matched scholarship with a practical and inventive mind, working from a young age in a millwright's workshop. In 1784 he headed south to work with James Watt at the Soho Birmingham works, and was responsible for installing steam engines at Albion Flour Mills in London, an early application of steam power to industrial production.

Setting up his own practice, Rennie was recommended by the very busy Jessop as engineer for the Lancaster Canal. This was followed by the Crinan and, the project he is best known

Dundas Aqueduct on the Kennet & Avon Canal

for, the Kennet & Avon, including the much admired Dundas Aqueduct near Bath.

Concurrently Rennie was very involved with dock schemes, and bridge-building, frequently using the new material, iron. In this he was followed by his son, also John, knighted for his work on London Bridge, which he built to his father's design.

Thomas Telford 1757–1834

The son of a shepherd, Telford was born into a tiny, isolated community on the Scottish borders. Within months of his birth, his father died, compounding the family's humble circumstances; nevertheless, with help from an uncle, the young Telford received a rudimentary village school education, which he followed with an apprenticeship to a local mason. His unlikely ambition was to be an architect.

After spells in Edinburgh, London and Portsmouth, Telford had a lucky break; a childhood friend, William Johnstone, married an heiress from Bath, adopting her family name, Pulteney. William Pulteney's estates included a castle in Shrewsbury, which Telford was commissioned to repair and improve. He was also offered the post of county surveyor for Shropshire. In this role he was responsible for all the county's bridges, including Abraham Darby's newly built and revolutionary Ironbridge over the Severn. The master mason soon developed a keen interest in the new material.

However, it was another offer that took him away from architecture into engineering. In Ellesmere, a group of businessmen had put forward a proposal for a canal to link the industrial areas around Ruabon and Wrexham with the River Dee at Chester. The group had already appointed Jessop as their chief engineer, and despite Telford's total lack of canal experience, he was offered a secondary post. Jessop was an extremely busy man and seems to have been happy to leave the planning to Telford, though he must take credit for approving Telford's radical approach.

A section of the Pontcysyllte Aqueduct, carrying the Llangollen Canal across the River Dee

Although the original concept of the Ellesmere Canal was never realised, it gave birth to one of the engineering wonders of the world. The original plan saw the canal heading north to Ruabon. This was aborted as the terrain was considered too difficult, and tramways were utilised instead. Before the decision was made, the plan had been for the canal to cross the River Dee, east of Llangollen, via a set of locks down and up the valley sides. But instead of locks, Telford proposed an aqueduct 120 feet high. This unprecedented design was made possible by replacing the conventional very heavy 'puddled' clay construction with a much lighter 'trough' of cast-iron plates bolted together.

Pontcysyllte is famous as the first iron aqueduct. It may have been the first planned, but by the time it was open, both Outram (at Derby) and Telford himself (at Longdon-upon-Tern) had working iron aqueducts in place.

Telford went on to build more canals, but is famous also for building roads and bridges as well as harbours, churches and even a new town. As the pace of the Industrial Revolution quickened, so Telford made his canals work harder: his re-routing of Brindley's Birmingham Navigations makes the 'Old Main Line' look like a country lane, while Telford's 'New Main Line' is a motorway by comparison. To compete with the coming railways, the Birmingham & Liverpool Junction Canal (today known as the Shropshire Union) was built as level and straight as the railways themselves, through massive cuttings and on high banks.

Another project in partnership with Jessop which continued until the latter's death was the Caledonian Canal, which runs from coast to coast through the Highlands. The scale was unprecedented in Britain at the time and was akin to the French Canal du Midi, being wide enough for oceangoing ships.

Today we look back on Telford as a genius, and we know of his reputation as a modest man. He thrived on hard work, and his character is coloured by the loyalty shown him by his teams of assistants and navvies. So it is strange to find no mention in his autobiography of the role of William Jessop, his superior at Ellesmere and his partner on the Caledonian – an apparent slight that no one has explained satisfactorily. This is not the place to explore this conundrum, which is discussed in my book *Thomas Telford's Scotland* and explored more fully in Charles Hadfield's *Thomas Telford's Temptation*, published in 1993.

Beyond

By the middle of the nineteenth century, the golden age of canals was over, the Birmingham & Liverpool Junction signalling the end of an era. There were further flourishes – notably the Sharpness Canal, bypassing the dangerous tidal Severn below Gloucester, and the Manchester Ship Canal. Both ventures enabled seagoing ships to extend the life of inland ports. Inventiveness did not die, and a latterday pioneer deserves a mention: Sir Edward Leader Williams (1824–1910), who built the Anderton Lift and then the Manchester Ship Canal.

As declining traffic caused the canals to struggle, the railways, now consolidated into big business groups, often bought canals that were local to their routes in order to snuff out competition. Once abandoned, the canals soon became unserviceable, turning into rough lines of weedy enclosures, rubbish dumps and stagnant ponds.

And so finally to one more pioneer: Tom Rolt, best known as the biographer of Victorian engineers, who in 1947, with the inland waterway system largely abandoned, challenged British Waterways over the right to navigate the Stratford Canal. It was his victory, and the subsequent setting up of the Inland

Waterways Association, that was to inspire a movement to restore derelict canals as places of leisure and recreation.

Six decades on, it is something of a miracle that British Waterways (itself about to be reconfigured, and facing an uncertain future) has in the late twentieth century, and on to today, been able to respond to the restoration movement, adding its expertise and funding to the enthusiasm of myriad groups of volunteers. The success of a hugely restored canal network can be measured by the claim that there are more boats on the canals today than there were at the height of commercial operation in 1820!

Barton swing bridge, Manchester Ship Canal

A typical Brindley spillway: Stewponey, on the Staffordshire & Worcestershire Canal

2

BRINDLEY, BIRMINGHAM & THE GRAND CROSS

The success of the Bridgewater Canal led industrialists such as Wedgwood and Arkwright to consider how this form of transport could benefit their businesses. Steam was beginning to replace water power, and increased productivity meant more goods to get to market; the increased demand for raw materials also strained existing supply lines, and manufacturers welcomed with open arms the prospect of reliable transport, not dependent on the country's appalling road system. Brindley was not short of ideas, summing up his proposals for more canals with his 'Grand Cross': a set of new waterways joining Britain's four main navigable rivers, the Thames, Severn, Trent and Mersey. The main artery in this bold new network was to be the Trent & Mersey Canal, named by Brindley the 'Grand Trunk'.

The completion of the Trent & Mersey was delayed by the construction of the tunnel at Harecastle Hill, opening in 1777 five years after Brindley's death. Meanwhile, the link to the Severn, the Staffordshire & Worcestershire, had reached the Severn at Stourport, a completely new town created to service the docks. The remaining river of Brindley's quartet was the Thames, but this proved more complicated, funding problems delaying the through-route, which finally opened in 1790.

Unlike any other major city, Birmingham, which was heavily industrialised from the mid-eighteenth century, has no river, so canal development there was early and particularly appropriate. Birmingham was not part of Brindley's concept, but if his 'Grand Cross' were the spokes of a wheel, the city would be its hub. The 'Main Line', built by Brindley and opened in 1772, was the city's chief transport artery. Several subsidiary canals led from it, connecting both to the north-east and to the west to meet the 'Grand Cross' canals. Subsequent modernisation has left Brindley's levels as feeders and loops serving old industrial sites.

Later additions such as the Stratford, Worcester & Birmingham, and Grand Union canals create in Gas Street Basin a sort of Clapham Junction of inland waterways. To drop out of the city centre's steel-and-glass bustle onto an old-time cobbled towpath and the timeless serenity of the narrowboats is to enter a parallel universe.

Bridgewater Canal: Worsley

Top left: The Packet House at Worsley was the original depot for parcels and a terminal for passengers.

Above: At Worsley Delph, this entrance to the Duke of Bridgewater's mines leads to miles of underground channels. The padlocked gate (left) reflects the fact that entry is restricted by the coal authority, though there is talk of restoration and open access to the public.

Facing page: Also at Worsley, the canal's original dry dock is still in active use.

Bridgewater Canal: Barton

Above: Sir Edward Leader Williams' 1894 aqueduct over the Manchester Ship Canal at Barton replaced Brindley's earlier aqueduct over the River Irwell.

Left: A remaining archway of Brindley's aqueduct acts as an abutment to the later structure.

Right: A 'stop board', for isolating sections of canal, on the Bridgewater at Barton.

Facing page: The aqueduct swings open for a boat on the Ship Canal (see also page 140).

*Trent & Mersey Canal:
Northwich*

*Above: A narrowboat
brokers' yard adjacent to a
local salt-processing plant.
Northwich is a centre of the
salt industry.*

*Right: Lion Works, a famous local
factory by the canal, is to become
a museum.*

*Facing page: The Anderton
Lift, built in 1875 by Sir
Edward Leader Williams,
replaced inclined planes
connecting the River Weaver
to the canal. The lift was
closed due to corrosion in 1983
and restored and re-opened
in 2001.*

Left: British Waterways 'helmsman' Mel Bryan inspecting the roof of Telford's tunnel.

Below left: A bone-grinding mill at Cheddleton, near Stoke-on-Trent, on the Chaldon branch canal. Crushed bone is an important constituent of bone china.

Facing page: A bone and flint mill at Etruria, original site of Wedgwood factories.

Trent & Mersey Canal: Staffordshire

Above: Harecastle Hill tunnels, north portals. Telford's tunnel, on the left, was intended to supplement Brindley's original on the right, offering one-way working, but the latter's dangerous state forced it to be abandoned.

Trent & Mersey Canal:
Leicestershire

Far left: The wharves at Shardlow
Basin, close to the junction with
the River Trent, are a mixture of
abandoned commercial buildings
and burgeoning middle-class
domesticity. Today, Shardlow is less
an inland port and more a pretty
tourist destination.

Left: Warehouse doors,
Shardlow Basin.

Below left: Heavy lock gate,
Swarkestone.

Facing page: Warehouse, Shardlow.

Staffordshire & Worcestershire Canal: Worcestershire

Above: Falling Sands Viaduct on the Severn Valley Railway.

Left: Caldwell Lock, Kidderminster, showing a typical cutting through red rock country, which continues some miles north.

Facing page: At Stourport Basin a completely new town was built around the connection to the River Severn.

Staffordshire & Worcestershire Canal
Kidderminster

Above: At Kidderminster wharfside,
industrial buildings have been turned
to modern usage.

Left: Bratch Locks, side ponds and an
unusual tollhouse.

Facing page: Stewponey Wharf.

Fazeley Canal

Above: Fazeley Toll House.

Facing page: At Fazeley Junction with Coventry Canal, the canal runs under the bridge to Birmingham city centre.

Coventry Canal: Hawkesbury Junction

Above: A narrowboat executes a 180° turn, leaving the Oxford Canal to continue north on the Coventry.

Left: Oxford Canal top lock.

Facing page: A wide view of the two canals, with the Coventry Canal on the left.

Oxford Canal

Above: Boatyard at Napton.

Left: View south from Napton Hill.

Facing page: Thrupp.

Oxford Canal

Left: The blacksmith's shop at Tooley's boatyard, Banbury.

Above: A belt-drive photographed in the workshop where Rolt's boat Cressy *was fitted for his 1939 journey (see page 17).*

Facing page: Banbury centre with Tooley's yard.

Birmingham Navigations

Above: Titford Engine House, home to the Birmingham Canal Society.

Left: Titford Canal passes under the M5 motorway.

Top left: Gas Street, central Birmingham.

Below left: 'Split bridge' at Factory Locks.

Facing page: Factory Locks and side ponds.

The Rochdale Canal crosses the Pennine watershed at Summit.

3

CROSSING THE PENNINES

Brindley's 'Grand Cross' was great news for factories close to its constituent canals. However, a very large proportion of industry was situated in the hilly country where Lancashire meets Yorkshire, where every valley has a town and every town has a mill. It could be argued that the Trent & Mersey reached from coast to coast, but it did not help the Pennine communities at all. To the east of Leeds, the Aire & Calder Navigation, connecting Leeds to the Humber, had been in use for a century; more recently, an extension, John Smeaton's Calder & Hebble, linked this route from the sea back up to Sowerby Bridge and to Huddersfield. This ready-made connection to the sea awaited any cross-Pennine canal.

The Leeds & Liverpool, engineered by Robert Whitworth and opened in 1801, takes a northern route from Liverpool, needing only a short tunnel at Foulridge north of Burnley to cross the watershed. Heading further north still, it crosses the headwaters of the Aire just south of Gargrave, where it swings east through the mill towns of Keighly and Shipley, heading for Leeds.

At Summit, following surveys by Brindley and William Jessop, John Rennie took charge of the Rochdale Canal opening in 1800; it takes a more direct line on its way to Sowerby Bridge, yet manages to cross the hills between Littleborough and Todmorden with no tunnel at all! This is not because Rennie was shy of tunnelling, but for financial reasons. He had already stretched the budget by making it a broad canal; adding extra locks and raising the summit level saved considerable funds.

Plans for a more direct route to the east side of Manchester led to Benjamin Outram's construction of the Huddersfield Narrow Canal, which opened in 1811. The main feature of this canal is the Standedge Tunnel, the highest, deepest and longest in Britain. Because the narrow canal meant delays at locks (and one-way working in the tunnel), the Halifax was never such a success as the Rochdale.

Just south of the Cromford Canal's terminus at Richard Arkwright's factory at High Peak Junction, an incline heading north is evidence of a more pragmatic approach to crossing the hills: these are the rails of the High Peak Railway, destination Whaley Bridge and a connection with the Peak Forest Canal.

Aire & Calder Navigation

Left: Central Leeds, where the Navigation meets the Leeds & Liverpool.

Above: Stanley Ferry Aqueduct, detail, where the canal crosses the River Calder.

Facing page: A wide view of Stanley Ferry with, on the left, its modern by-pass aqueduct.

Leeds & Liverpool Canal, Saltaire Mills

Left: A view back towards Saltaire from the top of Bingley 'five rise' locks.

Facing page: Saltaire Mills.

Leeds & Liverpool

Above: Priest Holme Aqueduct – a long view with daisies in the foreground.

Right: Boaters rest at Priest Holme where the canal crosses the headwaters of the River Aire.

Facing page: Skipton.

Overleaf: The River Aire, from the left of the picture, crosses under the Priest Holme Aqueduct.

Leeds & Liverpool: Burnley

Above: Burnley, Weavers' District.

Right: At Burnley Bank a mile-long straight on a high bank divides the town. During World War Two this section of canal was drained for fear of bomb damage flooding the town.

Facing page: Warehouses and wharf machinery at Burnley Weavers' District.

Leeds & Liverpool

Left: Stop board at Leigh, where the Leeds & Liverpool meets the Bridgewater.

Above: Terminal warehouses at Wigan.

Facing page: The coal-loading wharves of Wigan Pier commented on by George Orwell in his bleak look at the working north of England, are long since demolished. Today the district is dominated by night clubs, bars and a museum.

Rochdale Canal

*Above: The canal cuts
a green swathe through
the town's suburbs.*

Right: Summit, detail.

*Facing page: At Summit,
the Roch Aqueduct carries
the river over the canal
and railway.*

Rochdale Canal

Warehouses line the canal at Hebden Bridge (left) and Sowerby Bridge (above).

Top right: Todmarden, guillotine lock gate.

Facing page: George Stephenson's rail bridge at Gauxholme.

Huddersfield Narrow Canal

Above: Lift bridge, Huddersfield.

Left: Standedge Tunnel, east portal.

Facing page: Stalybridge Junction with Ashton Canal, leading to Peak Forest Canal.

Peak Forest Canal

Above: Marple Bridge, detail.

Left: Whaley Bridge, High Peak rail and canal interchange.

Facing page: Ruins at Buxworth Basin. Both Whaley Bridge and Buxworth were linked to the High Peak Railway (see overleaf).

Cromford Canal

Richard Arkwright was an advocate of canals, but changed his views when he realised they threatened the water supply to his mills. The terminus of the Cromford Canal is adjacent to his factory.

Far left: Leawood pump engine house.

Above: Warehouse at High Peak Junction.

Left: On this section of the High Peak Railway, trains were rope-hauled up the incline – a pragmatic solution to crossing the High Peak.

Facing page: Arkwright's mill at Cromford.

Entering Trevor Basin, from Pontcysyllte

4

Extending The Network

The realisation of Brindley's 'Grand Cross' scheme provided the country with a framework of trunk canals. But rather like a newly begun spider's web, it had an awful lot of gaps. Helping fill the gaps were the Worcester & Birmingham (1815) and the Stratford, both providing alternative choices for traffic from Britain's manufacturing heartland to the prime transport artery, the River Severn.

Important routes were cut in Wales and in Scotland. Neither connected with other canals, but the Monmouth & Brecon reached the sea at Newport, while the Forth & Clyde went from coast to coast, later to be extended by the Union. Also in Scotland, the Crinan provided a serious shortcut on the west coast, heading north from Greenock.

The canal known today as the Llangollen was originally the Ellesmere Canal; its genesis is a complicated story, and it follows a complicated route (see page 13). The muddled progress of this canal that never achieved its aims is completely overshadowed by the Pontcysyllte Aqueduct across the River Dee – a work of genius by Telford that is today a Unesco World Heritage Site.

Today there is almost no trace of the Shrewsbury or the Shropshire canals, but both have engineering treasures. On the line of the Shrewsbury at Longdon–upon-Tern, Thomas Telford's first lightweight aqueduct stands unnoticed in a farmer's field. It is tempting to see it as a prototype for Pontcysyllte, but, though built first, it was in fact planned second. The Shropshire, a very localised set of small boat canals, has, in Blists Hill Museum in Telford, the remains of a lift which took boats down to Coalport on the River Severn.

It might seem that every canal in the country is in the north, but finally it is important to include one of several that connected to the Thames: the Kennet & Avon. Engineered by John Rennie, the route can claim coast-to-coast status. Leaving the Thames with the Kennet at Reading, it heads past Newbury and Hungerford into rural Wiltshire, joining the Avon where it becomes navigable at Bath. Notable features on the line include two historic pumping stations, two of Rennie's classic aqueducts and a celebrated flight of locks at Caen. Derelict by the mid-twentieth century, the Kennet & Avon Canal was an early example of restoration, being re-opened by the Queen in 1990.

Shrewsbury Canal

Left: At the aqueduct at Longdon-upon-Tern, the remains of Clowes' heavy brick-built and clay-lined structure are still connected to Telford's lightweight iron trough aqueduct (facing page). This historic site stands unnoticed in a farmer's field.

Shropshire Canal

Above: Incline headframe at Blists Hill Museum, Coalbrookdale.

Left: Coalport factory by the River Severn, at the foot of the incline.

Facing page: This incline carried boats down to the level of the River Severn: the short canal at the base had wharves adjacent to the Coalport factory, but no connection to the river.

Monmouthshire & Brecon Canal

Far left: Brecon canal basin.

Left: Goytre lime kilns.

Below left: Two 'drams' at Llanfoist incline.

Facing page: Re-enactment for a UNESCO film, near Gilwern.

Forth & Clyde and Union Canals

Left: Linlithgow Basin, Union.

Above: Bowling sea lock, Forth and Clyde, on the Clyde estuary.

Facing page: Slateford Aqueduct crossing the Waters of Leith, on the Union Canal.

The junction of the two canals is today effected by the Falkirk Wheel (see page 144).

Crinan Canal

This short canal allows northbound shipping from Greenock to avoid going south round Kyntyre.

Above: Running by the sea, Sound of Jura.

Right: Cog and lighthouse, Ardrishaig.

Facing page: Ardrishaig.

Llangollen (originally Ellesmere) Canal

The Ellsmere never met its initial aims. One branch was truncated, another became the main line and the projected main route was turned into a tramway. However, the northern stretch from Chester to Ellesmere Port, a new town on the Mersey (above), was a great success.

Left: At Weston Lulling-fields the branch to the Severn never reached the river, terminating at the tiny hamlet of Weston Lullingfields. The route into North Wales successfully connected with the Montgomeryshire Canal at Llanymynych.

Below left: Still to be seen on the wharf at Trevor Basin are the rails of the tramway that replaced the canal's aborted Ruabon main line.

Facing page: Telford constructed Horshoe Falls in the Dee above Llangollen to keep a level of water in the supply feeder to Trevor Basin (which doubles as a navigable line to Llangollen).

Llangollen Canal: Ellesmere Town

Above and right: The canal company HQ and dry dock at Ellesmere Town.

Facing page: Wharfside machinery beside a branded warehouse of the Shropshire Union.

Llangollen Canal: Chirk

Above: Tunnel entrance at Chirk, with, for the time, the unusual provision of a towpath.

Right: Chirk Aqueduct, crossing the Ceiriog valley, would be celebrated if it were not in the shadow of Pontcysyllte (see following pages).

Facing page: Aqueduct, and subsequent railway viaduct, seen from above the tunnel.

Llangollen Canal: Pontcysyllte

Telford's unprecedented masterpiece is today a UNESCO World Heritage Site.

Above: Boats in the mist.

Right: A view of the aqueduct from downstream on the River Dee.

Facing page: A view across the valley, with sheep.

Worcester &
Birmingham Canal

Above: Tardebigge, top lock.

Top right: Ducks and residential boats, Hanbury Wharf.

Right: Tardebigge engine house.

Facing page: Diglis Basin on the River Severn at Worcester is a purpose-built canal development.

Worcester & Birmingham Canal: Kings Norton, Birmingham

Far left: Stop board at junction with Stratford Canal.

Left: 'Worcester Bar', where the original barrier prevented through traffic from Worcester going beyond Gas Street.

Facing page: The stop board and bar are reminders of how jealously the canal companies protected their water supply.

Stratford Canal

Above: Hockley Heath lift bridge

Left: Edstone Aqueduct, seen from below.

Facing page: Edstone Aqueduct panorama.

Stratford Canal

*Above and right: The split bridge
and round-roofed lock house, both at
Kingswood Junction, are typical of
this canal.*

*Facing page: Breakfast at Stratford
Canal Basin, with the Royal Shakespeare
Theatre in the background.*

*Overleaf: On the Ashby Canal,
Moira furnace and engine house are
today beyond the navigable part of
the canal.*

Kennet & Avon Canal

Left: Bath elegance and canal cobbled vernacular, close to the junction with the River Avon.

Far left: Cleveland House, the canal company HQ, was built over the canal in Sydney Gardens. A trapdoor in the floor allowed tolls and paperwork to be handled without the boat being moored.

Facing page: Sydney Gardens features elegant cast-iron pedestrian bridges from Coalbrookdale.

Kennet & Avon

Above: At Claverton, Rennie took an old water mill and converted it to a water-driven water pump supplying the canal.

Right: Residential boats on the wharves of the remaining length of the Somerset Coal Canal.

Facing page: Avoncliff, one of two Rennie aqueducts on this stretch of canal (see page 12).

Kennet & Avon

*Above: Crofton pumping station,
near Hungerford.*

*Right: Beams of the pair of 'Cornish'
engines, Boulton & Watt of 1812,
supplemented by Harvey's of Hale.*

*Facing page: Stoking the 1845
Lancashire boiler with its
double firebox.*

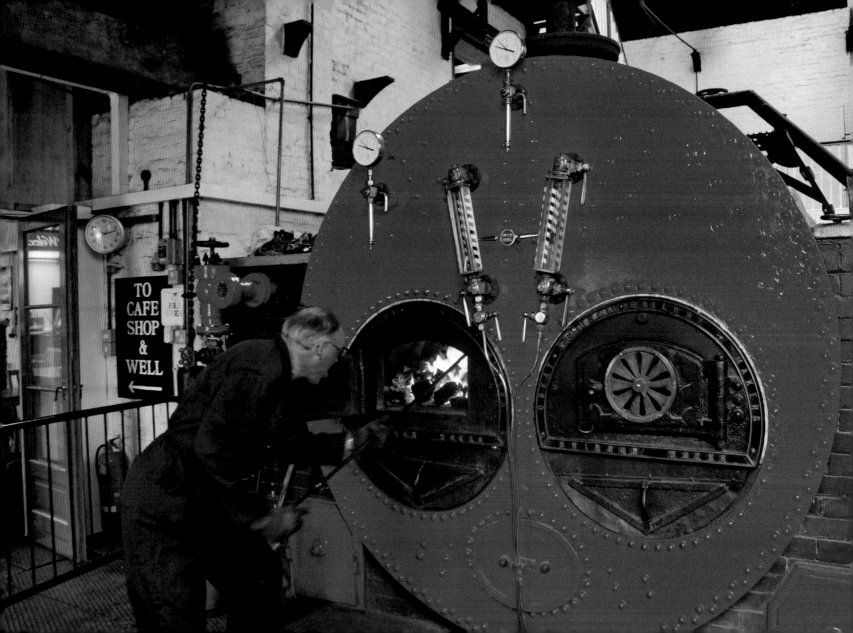

TO
CAFE
SHOP
& WELL
←

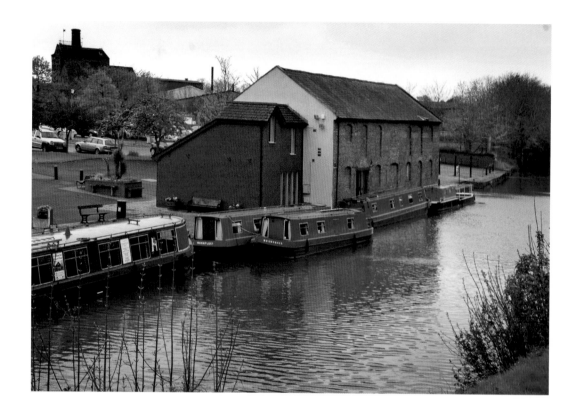

Kennet & Avon

Left: At Devizes Wharf, this warehouse is now used as a theatre.

Facing page: Working a lock below the celebrated Caen flight.

Kennet & Avon

Left: The less salubrious end of Reading, where the canal joins the Thames.

Below: Monkey Marsh lock, one of two with turf construction.

Facing page: The modernised canal runs through Reading's glass and chrome Oracle Centre.

This original swing bridge is on the Caledonian Canal at Moy.

5
FINAL FLOURISH

Before the end of the seventeenth century it was clear that delays on the canal system were costing business. Well before the threat of competition from the railways, attempts were made to by-pass some of Brindley's early 'contour' canals. Others were improved, with broad locks replacing narrow, while the use of deep cuttings, lowering and lengthening summit levels, also meant fewer locks.

While there were several choices of route for Birmingham traffic to take southbound, they mostly led to the Severn; the only way to reach London was down the Oxford Canal to the Thames, where the twin hazards of flood and water shortage plagued the bargees. In 1790, William Jessop was asked to survey a new line, to be called Grand Junction, from the Thames at Brentford to Braunston on the Oxford Canal, which would open in 1805. Even during construction the route was improved with an extension to Paddington in west London. This in turn was extended east across north London to Limehouse Docks on the River Thames.

The project to create a better line north from Birmingham to the Mersey was triggered by talk of a railway planned for that route. Telford was asked to counter that threat: his new line would be broad-beam; tunnels would have towpaths, and locks would be kept to a minimum by extensive use of cuttings and embankments. It would be the ultimate inland waterway. If that didn't stop the railways, nothing would – and of course nothing did.

By 1830, even bigger canals were being built for seagoing ships: the Gloucester & Berkeley (today known as the Sharpness Canal) and the Caledonian both operating. A latecomer of a pioneering engineer, Sir Edward Leader Williams, already famous for his Anderton Lift, was in 1894 engineer to Britain's ultimate waterway, the Manchester Ship Canal. The River Irwell was totally subsumed into the new, wider channel: to replace Brindley's Bridgewater Canal crossing, Leader Williams designed a unique swing aqueduct.

So the centuries tick by, and the inventive spirit that the canals seem to engender still has a trick to offer. As a millennium project, the long-derelict locks that linked the two canals in central Scotland were replaced by a huge rotating lift. Opened by the Queen in 2002 as part of her golden jubilee celebration, today the Falkirk Wheel does a wonderful job of showing off British inventiveness, though it is visited by far more tourists than boaters!

Birmingham Navigations

Crossing the 'New Main Line', celebrated Telford works include Galton Bridge (above) and the Engine Arm Aqueduct (right).

Facing page: Smethwick Pumping House, showing two levels of canal following Telford's improvements.

Grand Union (formerly Grand Junction) Canal

Left: A boat-weighing machine on display at the canal museum at Stoke Bruerne.

Above: Hatton: the original narrow lock, now a spillway, was replaced by one for broad-beam boats to the left.

Right: Blisworth Tunnel, north portal

Facing page: One of several vents above Blisworth Tunnel.

Grand Union Canal

Above: Gayton, with Robert Stephenson's railway.

Top right: Braunston Yard.

Right: Pedestrian tunnel under the huge embankment by the 'Iron Trunk'.

Facing page: The 'Iron Trunk': detail of the replacement aqueduct at Wolverton, crossing the River Ouse.

Grand Union Canal, Paddington Arm

Far left: At Paddington waterside, a huge steel-and-glass development dwarfs a visiting narrowboat.

Above: This timber yard still operates in Paddington basin but no longer uses the wharf.

Left: Windmill Bridge, built by Brunel to take his railway and the road over the canal on three levels.

Facing page: Bulls Bridge, where the Grand Union divides, to Brentford and to Paddington.

 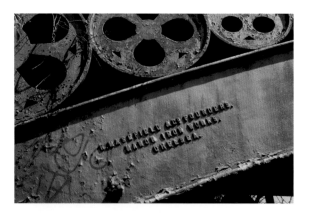

Regents Canal: Little Venice to
Regents Park.

Views of Regents Park bridges.
Right: Iron columns of Macclesfield
Bridge. Top right: Footbridge from a
Chelsea ironworks. Above: Shining
rivets under Stephenson's Birmingham
Railway.

Facing page: A view towards Little
Venice from Café Laville, above the
entrance to Maida Hill Tunnel.

Regents Canal

Right: Parties of schoolchildren line the banks beyond the crowds in the Camden waterside market.

Facing page: From Little Venice to Camden lock is the most popular trip on the whole network.

Grand Union, Leicester Branch

Left: Iron barge on display at the canal museum in Foxton.

Above: Foxton Locks

Facing page: Foxton Incline is undergoing restoration.

Shropshire Union (formerly Birmingham & Liverpool Junction) Canal

Left: Lock gear and tollhouse at the junction with the Staffordshire & Worcestershire Canal at Autherley.

Above: Telford's canal crossing his Holyhead Road at Stretton Aqueduct.

Facing page: Iron mileage sign at Autherley.

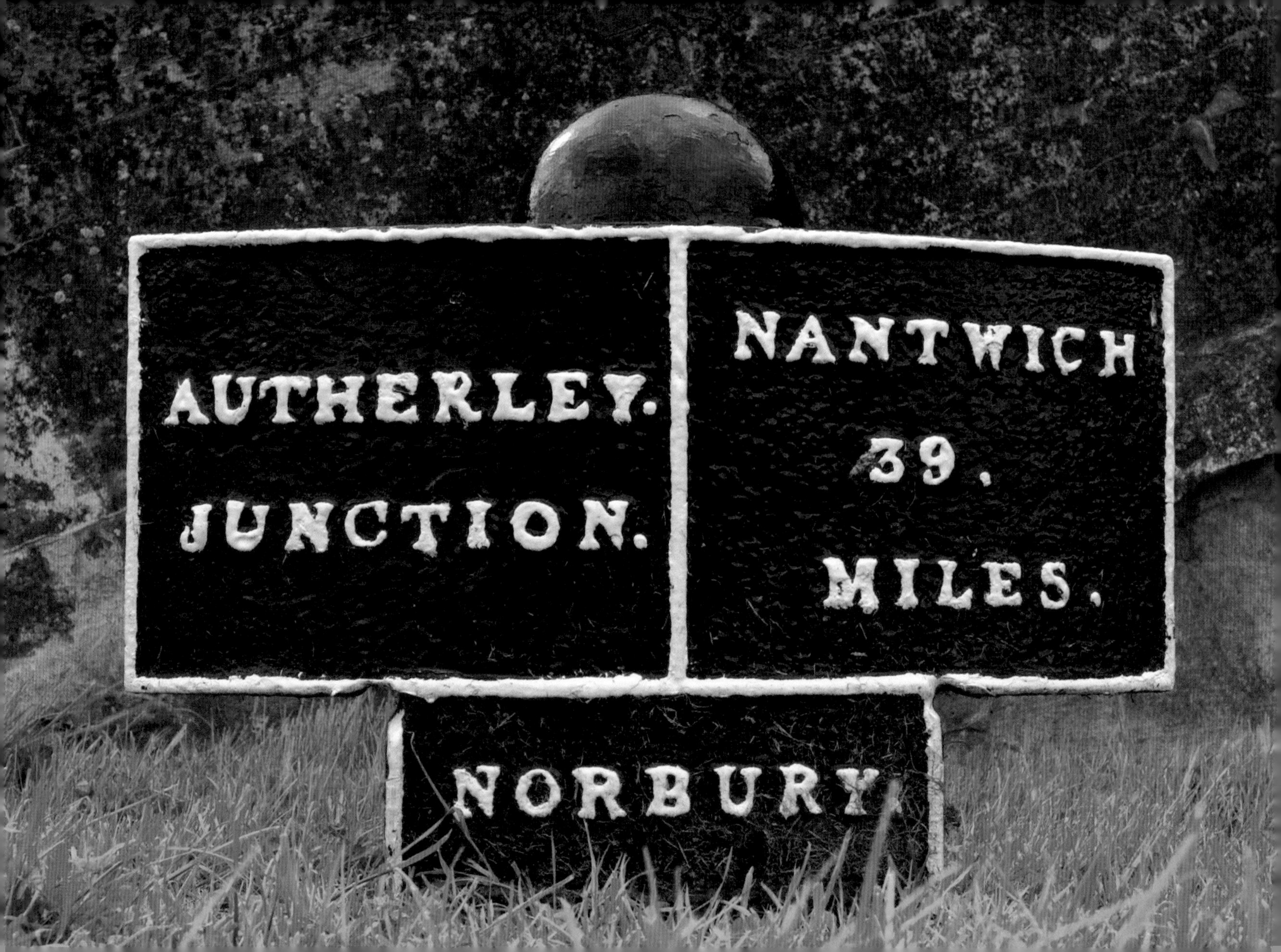
AUTHERLEY.
JUNCTION.
NANTWICH
39.
MILES.
NORBURY.

Shropshire Union (formerly Birmingham & Liverpool Junction) Canal

Telford's reluctance to deviate from a straight and level route required high embankments and deep cuttings which need regular maintenance.

Above: A high embankment at Shelmore.

Top left: A deep rock cutting at Tyrley.

Left: A British Waterways maintenance boat.

Facing page: Cowley Tunnel.

Sharpness Canal (formerly the Gloucester & Berkeley)

Above: Sharpness Dock is still used for bulk cargoes.

Left: Pleasure boats en route to Upton Marina in the Sharpness tidal lock on the Severn.

Facing page: Sharpness old lock entrance and harbourmaster's house are now used by river rescue teams.

Sharpness Canal

Above: Bridge keepers' houses on the Sharpness Canal have quaint classical columns.

Right: The abutments are all that remain of the Severn Railway Bridge. The right-hand tower carried the pivoting swing section over the canal.

Facing page: Commerce mingles with residential narrowboats near Saul.

Sharpness Canal

Left: A modern lift bridge at the south end of Gloucester Docks.

Above: The Mariners' Chapel, Gloucester Docks.

Facing page: Warehouses at Gloucester Docks.

Caledonian Canal

Above: RNLI lifeboat in Neptune's Staircase, en route from Isla to Buckie.

Left: View towards Ben Nevis, from the top of Neptune's Staircase.

Facing page: The Caledonian Canal heads up the Great Glen, past Moy and Loy.

Caledonian Canal

Left: The canal, high on a massive embankment, crossing the River Loy.

Facing page: Andrew Walker, now retired, works the only original swing bridge at Moy.

Caledonian Canal

Above: VIC32, a 'Clyde Puffer' moored in the basin below Clachnaharry.

Top right: A flight of locks at Fort Augustus.

Right: The River Garry provides the canal's water supply into Loch Oich.

Facing page: Laggan Cutting, its depth masked by the forest.

Manchester Ship Canal

Above: Barton Aqueduct carries the Bridgewater Canal over the Manchester Ship Canal. The control tower controls both the aqueduct and the adjacent road bridge (right).

Top right: Nick Moreton, one of thirteen operatives needed for every passage up and down the canal.

Facing page: Part of the original aqueduct swing mechanism on which the vast trough of water pivots.

Manchester Ship Canal

Above: Warehouses at Salford.

*Facing page: View over the Barton
Aqueduct to Manchester.*

Boat Lift

Above: The twenty-first-century Falkirk Wheel replaced eleven derelict locks linking the Union and the Forth & Clyde Canals.

Dauntsey Lock on the Berkshire & Wiltshire Canal, before restoration

6
DERELICTION AND RESTORATION

In 1936, canal enthusiast Tom Rolt bought a narrowboat, *Cressy*, with the intention of living aboard on an extended canal cruise. After having it extensively altered and renovated at Tooley's Yard in Banbury (see page 38), he and his wife set off in 1939, planning to document the way of life on the waterways. Delayed by the war, in 1944 he published the account of his travels in a book entitled *Narrow Boat*. This produced a ripple of interest in the tiny pool of canal enthusiasts. By 1947 extensive stretches of the canal system were virtually abandoned, but legally the owners still had to respect the right of navigation. Rolt challenged British Waterways for the right of passage under a bridge on the Stratford Canal that had been built almost down to water level. His victory saw the bridge having to be jacked up to allow *Cressy* through. This episode, and the subsequent setting up of the Inland Waterways Association, inspired and invigorated a movement to restore the canals and where possible, return them to use for leisure and recreation.

Anyone who thinks restoration is achievable by the efforts of a few volunteers with pickaxes and wheelbarrows is not in touch with the reality and the sheer scale of earthworks required. To visit Stroud at the west end of the line of the Thames & Severn is to witness a major civil engineering project. Within the security fencing, the site is buzzing loudly with several diggers, while men with high-visibility jackets and theodolites check the progress of a new line being taken under the railway viaduct.

Historically, British Waterways has been supportive in funding and expertise; however, in 2002, the organisation itself faces an uncertain future. The difficulties that canal societies have to cope with seem to an outsider so daunting that it is admirable they are all so upbeat about eventual success. Of course, the historic successes are there to buoy them up, but it is also a fact that their sheer professionalism engenders a deserved optimism. It is this, coupled with enthusiasm and belief in a project, that provides the momentum to keep the movement rolling on.

Lancaster Canal

Above: Glasson, where the canal connects with the sea.

Top right: A rural scene in the high hills south of Kendal.

Right: Mother and buggy use the Lune Aqueduct as a jogging track.

Facing page: The River Lune Aqueduct, north of Lancaster.

Stroudwater Navigation

Above: A restored section east of the still-derelict Pike Lock.

Right: Burnt House Farm, Framilode. The name refers back to the riots sparked by the canal's construction. As in many other areas, local people feared the changes the canals would bring.

Facing page: The view north from Walk Bridge.

Thames & Severn Canal

Left: Brimscombe Mill is all that remains of what was once a large inland port.

Above: Ham Mill lock in the Chalford Valley.

Facing page: Major engineering work re-routing the canal out of Stroud.

Thames & Severn Canal

Above: Canal iced over in the cutting east of Sapperton

Centre: Marston Meysey round house, one of five remaining lock cottages built in this distinctive way.

Top right: Coates round house.

Far right: East portal, Sapperton Tunnel.

Facing page: Inglesham, where the Thames & Severn meets the River Thames.

Montgomeryshire Canal

Today this name includes the old Ellesmere Canal that linked up at Llanymynech (see page 78).

Above: Derelict lock cottage, Newtown.

Top left: Canal milepost at Brynderwern.

Left: Shropshire Union warehouse at Brynderwen.

Facing page: An abandoned canal bed, Newtown.

Montgomeryshire Canal

Left: Llanymynech, where the Ellesmere met the Montgomeryshire Canal.

Above: River Vyrnwy Aqueduct.

Right: Canalside machinery.

Facing page: Girls on the towpath opposite wharf buildings at Welshpool, now converted to a canal museum.

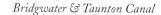

Bridgwater & Taunton Canal

Left: Buttresses decorated with 'bons mots', where the canal cuts through the town.

Below: 'Red Quantock' may not be a political slogan, but a reference to the red rocks.

Facing page: Bridgwater Dock connects the canal to the navigable River Parret and the sea. Brunel built a dredger to stop the dock silting up; presumably it was successful as he subsequently built one for Bristol.

Grand Western Canal and the Bridgwater

The plan for the Grand Western was to run from Taunton to Exeter, possibly embracing the Bridgwater. In the event, it only reached Tiverton, where a short section is navigable. The canal is historic for its use of vertical boat lifts, all now vanished except at Nynehead (left).

There was also an inclined plane at Wellisford (top left). Today this is not much more than a slope in a meadow, with the depleted canal running below (below left).

Facing page: Siesta by a Bridgwater lift bridge, with the M5 and Somerset Levels beyond.

Hereford & Gloucester Canal

Above: A section near the tunnel at Ashperton, not yet restored.

Right: Oxenhall Lock, restoration complete.

Left: Renewing a section adjacent to the River Severn.

Facing page: The team running the Wharf House restaurant, which is owned by the canal society. Profits from the restaurant go towards future restoration projects.

Index of Canals & Engineers

Canal	Engineer	Date opened	Canal	Engineer	Date opened
Aire & Calder Navigation	Hadley	2704	Kennet & Avon	Rennie	1810
Ashby	Whitby	1804	Lancaster	Rennie	1819
Ashton	Outram	1800	Lea Navigation (river improvement)	–	1425
Basingstoke	?	1794	Leeds & Liverpool	Whitworth	1801
Berkshire & Wiltshire	Whitworth	1810	Llangollen	Telford	?
Birmingham Navigations	Brindley	1772	Macclesfield	Telford?	1831
Brecon & Monmouth	Dadford	1800	Manchester Ship	Leader Williams	1894
Bridgewater	Brindley	1772	Montgomeryshire	Dadford	1797
Bridgwater & Taunton	Hollinsworth	1841	Oxford	Brindley	1790
Calder & Hebble Navigation	Smeaton	1767	Peak Forest	Outram	1800
Chester	Brindley	1779	Rochdale	Rennie	1800
Chesterfield	Henshall	1777	Sharpness (Gloucester & Berkeley)	Mylne	1827
Coventry	Brindley	1789	Shropshire	Reynolds	1792
Cromford	Jessop	1794	Shrophire Union (Main Line)	Telford	?
Erewash	Varley	1779	Staffordshire & Worcestershire	Brindley	1772
Exeter (river by-pass)	–	1566	Stratford-upon-Avon	Clowes	1802
Fossdyke	–	120 AD	Stroudwater	Priddy	1779
Grand Union	Jessop	1815	Thames & Severn	Clowes	1789
Grand Western	Thomas	1839	Trent & Mersey	Brindley	1771
Hereford & Gloucester	Clowes	1798	Worcester & Birmingham	Clowes	1815
Huddersfield Narrow	Outram	1811			

INDEX OF LOCATIONS

*Where appropriate, OS map references are given in **bold**.*

Further Reading

Burton, Anthony: *Canal 250: The Story of Britain's Canals* (The History Press Ltd, 2011)

Fisher, Stuart: *Canals of Britain: A Complete Guide* (Adlard Coles Nautical, 2009)

Household, Humphrey: *The Thames & Severn Canal* (Amberley Publishing, 2009)

Rolt, L.T.C.: *Narrow Boat* (The History Press Ltd, 2009)

Acknowledgements

My thanks are due to:

British Waterways
London Canal Museum
Stoke Bruerne Museum
Foxton Museum
Gloucester Waterways Museum
Canals, Rivers + Boats magazine
Peel Holdings plc

– and last but not least, my editor and designer, Paul Manning.

About the author

Photographer Chris Morris lives and works in the Forest of Dean. He is the author of several books combining documentary photography with his long-standing interest in industrial history.

The Great Brunel
978-0-9564358-1-1

The Stephensons: Railway Pioneers
978-0-9564358-0-4

Searching for Sir Humphrey
978-0-9542096-8-1

A Portrait of the Severn
978-0-9542096-5-0

Under Blorenge Mountain
978-0-9542096-1-2

Thomas Telford's Scotland
978-0-9542096-9-8